Date Due

W9-AMN-823

APR 18 1967	DEC. 17 1981	
MAY 1 1967	FEB. 22 1983	DE 9'87
MAY 1 1969	APR. 12 1983	
DEC 30 1969	NOV 1 1983	JA 5'88
8/08/69	NOV. 30 1983	AP 10'89
JUN 6 1971	JAN. 18 1984	NO 15 89
	FEB. 9 1984	
FEB 20 1975		DE 17'90
	MAR. 1 1984	JY 15'91
OCT 23 1975	OCT. 13 1984	AG 12'91
MAR 1975	OCT. 31 1984	AG 19'91
1976	DEC. 13 1984	AG 18'92
MAR 26 1976	AP 17'85	DE 17'92
NOV 23 1976	JE 11'85	NOV 18 94
DEC 6 1976	OCT. 30 1985	DEC 21 94
MAR 3 1978	NO 29'85	MAR 25 97
	FE 4'87	FE 15'01
NOV 11 1990	AG 14'87	NO 23 04
Demco 293-5	AP 24'08	FE 13'06

j
811.08
L

DE 02 06219

Larrick, Nancy
Poetry for holidays

EAU CLAIRE DISTRICT LIBRARY

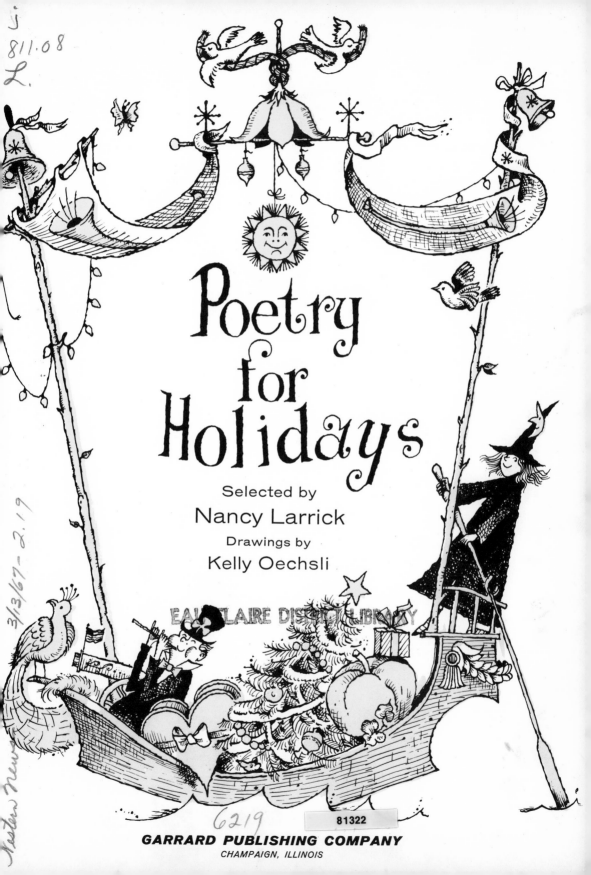

Poetry for Holidays

Selected by
Nancy Larrick
Drawings by
Kelly Oechsli

811.08
L.

3/3/67 - 2.19

EAU CLAIRE DISTRICT LIBRARY

6219   81322

GARRARD PUBLISHING COMPANY
CHAMPAIGN, ILLINOIS

The editor and publisher acknowledge with thanks permission received to reprint the poems in this collection.

Acknowledgments and formal notices of copyright for all material under copyright appear on pages 61 and 62 which are hereby made an extension of the copyright page.

Copyright © 1966 by Nancy Larrick

All rights reserved. Manufactured in the U.S.A.

Library of Congress Catalog Card Number: 66-10724

Poetry for Holidays

October Magic

I know
I saw
  a spooky witch
  out riding on her broom.

I know
I saw
  a goblin thing
  who's laughing in my room.

I think
  perhaps I saw a ghost
  who had a pumpkin face,
  and creepy cats
  and sleepy bats
  are hiding every place.

It doesn't matter where I look
There's something to be seen,

I know it is October
So I think it's Halloween.

Myra Cohn Livingston

What Night Would It Be?

If the moon shines
On the black pines
And an owl flies
And a ghost cries
And the hairs rise
On the back
  on the back
    on the back of your neck—

If you look quick
At the moon-slick
On the black air
And what goes there
Rides a broom-stick

And if things pick
At the back
  at the back
    at the back of your neck—

Would you know then
By the small men
With the lit grins
And with no chins,
By the owl's *hoo,*
And the ghost's *boo,*
By the Tom Cat,
And the Black Bat,
On the night air,
And the thing there,
By the thing,
  by the thing,
    by the dark thing there
(Yes, you do,
  yes, you do
    know the thing I mean)

That it's now,
  that it's now,
    that it's—Halloween!

John Ciardi

Hallowe'en

Tonight is the night
When dead leaves fly
Like witches on switches
Across the sky,
When elf and sprite
Flit through the night
On a moony sheen.

Tonight is the night
When leaves make a sound
Like a gnome in his home
Under the ground,
When spooks and trolls
Creep out of holes
Mossy and green.

Tonight is the night
When pumpkins stare
Through sheaves and leaves
Everywhere,
When ghoul and ghost
And goblin host
Dance round their queen.
It's Hallowe'en!

Harry Behn

Hallowe'en

Broomsticks and witches,
On Hallowe'en night
They fly over ditches
To meet other witches.
I *saw* 'em tonight.

Marchette Chute

Was She a Witch?

There was an old woman
Lived down in a dell;
She used to draw picklejacks
Out of the well.
How did she do it?
Nobody knew it,
She never, no never, no never
would tell.

Laura E. Richards

Halloween

The sky was yellow,
the moon was green,
and the little old Witch
whispered:

"Halloween!"

and, at the word,
from an ivied tower
thirteen black bats
in a black bat shower
came fluttering through
the pea-green gloom
and rested there
on the WITCH'S BROOM!

(And a Witch's Broom—
pray don't forget—
is a million times faster
than any JET!)
So they went to the moon,
and they circled about,
then they swept and they swept
till they swept it out;
they swept out the moon
and they made their flight—
THERE and BACK
in a single night.

Ivy O. Eastwick

This Is Halloween

Goblins on the doorstep,
  Phantoms in the air,
Owls on witches' gateposts
  Giving stare for stare,
Cats on flying broomsticks,
  Bats against the moon,
Stirrings round of fate-cakes
  With a solemn spoon,
Whirling apple parings,
  Figures draped in sheets
Dodging, disappearing,
  Up and down the streets,
Jack-o'-lanterns grinning,
  Shadows on a screen,
Shrieks and starts and laughter—
  This is Halloween!

Dorothy Brown Thompson

The Goblin

A goblin lives in *our* house, in *our* house, in *our* house,
A goblin lives in *our* house all the year round.
He bumps
And he jumps
And he thumps
And he stumps.
He knocks
And he rocks
And he rattles at the locks.
A goblin lives in *our* house, in *our* house, in *our* house,
A goblin lives in *our* house all the year round.

Rose Fyleman

The Witches' Ride

Over the hills
Where the edge of the light
Deepens and darkens
To ebony night,
Narrow hats high
Above yellow bead eyes,
The tatter-haired witches
Ride through the skies.
Over the seas
Where the flat fishes sleep
Wrapped in the slap of the slippery deep,
Over the peaks
Where the black trees are bare,
Where boney birds quiver
They glide through the air.
Silently humming
A horrible tune,
They sweep through the stillness
To sit on the moon.

Karla Kuskin

Jack-o'-Lantern

Jack-o'-lantern, Jack-o'-lantern,
orange-front-and-back-o'-lantern,
sitting-on-the-sill-o'-lantern,
where's your sister Jill-o'-lantern?

Aileen Fisher

What Am I?

They chose me from my brothers: "That's the
Nicest one," they said,
And they carved me out a face and put a
Candle in my head;

And they set me on the doorstep. Oh, the
Night was dark and wild;
But when they lit the candle, then I
Smiled!

Dorothy Aldis

Black and Gold

Everything is black and gold,
   Black and gold, tonight;
Yellow pumpkins, yellow moon,
   Yellow candlelight;

Jet-black cat with golden eyes,
   Shadows black as ink,
Firelight blinking in the dark
   With a yellow blink.

Black and gold, black and gold,
   Nothing in between—
When the world turns black and gold,
   Then it's Halloween!

Nancy Byrd Turner

I Like Fall

I like fall:
it always smells smoky,
chimneys wake early,
the sun is poky;

Folks go past
in a hustle and bustle,
and when I scuff
in the leaves, they rustle.

I like fall:
all the hills are hazy,
and after a frost
the puddles look glazy;

And nuts rattle down
where nobody's living,
and pretty soon . . .
it will be THANKSGIVING.

Aileen Fisher

Thanksgiving Day

Over the river and through the wood,
　To grandfather's house we go;
　　The horse knows the way
　　To carry the sleigh
Through the white and drifted snow.

Over the river and through the wood—
　Oh, how the wind does blow!
　　It stings the toes
　　And bites the nose,
　As over the ground we go.

Over the river and through the wood,
  To have a first-rate play.
    Hear the bells ring,
    "Ting-ling-ding!"
  Hurrah for Thanksgiving Day!

Over the river and through the wood
  Trot fast, my dapple-gray!
    Spring over the ground,
    Like a hunting-hound!
  For this is Thanksgiving Day.

Over the river and through the wood,
  And straight through the barnyard gate.
    We seem to go
    Extremely slow,—
  It is so hard to wait!

Over the river and through the wood—
  Now grandmother's cap I spy!
    Hurrah for the fun!
    Is the pudding done?
  Hurrah for the pumpkin pie!

Lydia Maria Child

From

Thanksgiving

I thank you, God,
That swallows know their way
In the great sky;
That grass, all brown today,
And dead and dry,
Will quiver in the sun
All green and gay
When Winter's done.

Louise Driscoll

December

I like days
with a snow-white collar,
and nights when the moon
is a silver dollar,
and hills are filled
with eiderdown stuffing
and your breath makes smoke
like an engine puffing.

I like days
when feathers are snowing,
and all the eaves
have petticoats showing,
and the air is cold
and the wires are humming,
But you feel all warm . . .
with Christmas coming.

Aileen Fisher

Christmas Eve

On a winter night
When the moon is low
The rabbits hop on the frozen snow.
The woodpecker sleeps in his hole in
    the tree
And fast asleep is the chickadee.

Twelve o'clock
And the world is still
As the Christmas star comes over the
    hill.
The angels sing, and sing again:
"Peace on earth, goodwill to men."

Marion Edey

Song

Why do bells for Christmas ring?
Why do little children sing?

Once a lovely, shining star,
Seen by shepherds from afar,
Gently moved until its light
Made a manger's cradle bright.

There a darling baby lay,
Pillowed soft upon the hay;
And its mother sang and smiled,
"This is Christ, the holy child!"

Therefore bells for Christmas ring,
Therefore little children sing.

Eugene Field

Long, Long Ago

Winds through the olive trees
    Softly did blow,
Round little Bethlehem
    Long, long ago.

Sheep on the hillside lay
    Whiter than snow;
Shepherds were watching them,
    Long, long ago.

Then from the happy sky,
    Angels bent low,
Singing their songs of joy,
    Long, long ago.

For in a manger bed,
    Cradled we know,
Christ came to Bethlehem,
    Long, long ago.

Unknown

Cradle Hymn

Away in a manger,
No crib for a bed,
The little Lord Jesus
Lay down his sweet head;
The stars in the heavens
Looked down where he lay,
The little Lord Jesus
Asleep on the hay.

The cattle are lowing,
The poor baby wakes,
But little Lord Jesus
No crying he makes.
I love thee, Lord Jesus,
Look down from the sky,
And stay by my cradle
Till morning is nigh.

Martin Luther

Words from
an Old Spanish Carol

Shall I tell you who will come
　　to Bethlehem on Christmas Morn,
Who will kneel them gently down
　　before the Lord, new-born?

One small fish from the river,
　　with scales of red, red gold,
One wild bee from the heather,
　　one grey lamb from the fold,
One ox from the high pasture,
　　one black bull from the herd,
One goatling from the far hills,
　　one white, white bird.

And many children, God give them grace,
bringing tall candles to light Mary's face.

Shall I tell you who will come
　　to Bethlehem on Christmas Morn,
Who will kneel them gently down
　　before the Lord, new-born?

Ruth Sawyer

Noël

Then be ye glad, good people,
   This night of all the year,
And light ye up your candles;
   His star is shining near.

From Old Besançon Noël

The Friendly Beasts

Jesus our brother, kind and good,
Was humbly born in a stable rude;
The friendly beasts around Him stood,
Jesus our brother, kind and good.

"I," said the donkey, shaggy and brown,
"I carried His Mother up hill and down;
I carried her safely to Bethlehem town,
I," said the donkey, shaggy and brown.

"I," said the cow, all white and red,
"I gave Him my manger for His bed;
I gave Him my hay to pillow His head.
I," said the cow, all white and red.

"I," said the sheep with the curly horn,
"I gave Him wool for a blanket warm.
He wore my coat on Christmas morn.
I," said the sheep with the curly horn.

"I," said the dove from the rafters high,
"I cooed Him to sleep so He would not cry,
I cooed Him to sleep, my mate and I.
I," said the dove from the rafters high.

And every beast, by some good spell,
In the stable dark was glad to tell,
Of the gift he gave Immanuel,
The gift he gave Immanuel.

Unknown

My Gift

What can I give Him
Poor as I am;
If I were a shepherd
I would a lamb,
If I were a Wise Man,
I would do my part.
Yet what can I give Him?
Give my heart.

Christina G. Rossetti

From

We Three Kings

We three kings of Orient are,
Bearing gifts we traverse afar,
   Field and fountain,
   Moor and mountain,
Following yonder star.
    O star of wonder, star of night
    Star with royal beauty bright;
      Westward leading,
      Still proceeding,
    Guide us to thy perfect light.

John Henry Hopkins

Carol of
the Brown King

Of the three Wise Men
Who came to the King,
One was a brown man,
So they sing.

Of the three Wise Men
Who followed the Star,
One was a brown king
From afar.

They brought fine gifts
Of spices and gold
In jeweled boxes
Of beauty untold.

Unto His humble
Manger they came
And bowed their heads
In Jesus' name.

Three Wise Men,
One dark like me—
Part of His
Nativity.

Langston Hughes

In the Week When Christmas Comes

This is the week when Christmas comes.

Let every pudding burst with plums,
And every tree bear dolls and drums,
   In the week when Christmas comes.

Let every hall have boughs of green,
With berries glowing in between,
   In the week when Christmas comes.

Let every doorstep have a song
Sounding the dark street along,
   In the week when Christmas comes.

Let every steeple ring a bell
With a joyful tale to tell,
   In the week when Christmas comes.

Let every night put forth a star
To show us where the heavens are,
   In the week when Christmas comes.

Let every stable have a lamb
Sleeping warm beside its dam,
   In the week when Christmas comes.

This is the week when Christmas comes.

Eleanor Farjeon

Beggar's Rhyme

Christmas is coming, the geese are getting
    fat,
Please to put a penny in an old man's hat;
If you haven't a penny, a ha'penny will
    do.
If you haven't got a ha'penny, God bless
    you.

Unknown

Christmas Stocking

What will go into the Christmas stocking
While the clock on the mantlepiece goes tick-tocking?

    An orange, a penny,
    Some sweets, not too many,
    A trumpet, a dolly,
    A sprig of red holly,
    A book and a top
    And a grocery shop,
    Some beads in a box,
    An ass and an ox
    And a lamb, plain and good,
    All whittled in wood,
    A white sugar dove,
    A handful of love,
    Another of fun,
    And it's very near done—
    A big silver star
    On top—there you are!

Come morning you'll wake up to the clock's tick-tocking,
And that's what you'll find in the Christmas stocking.

Eleanor Farjeon

The Christmas Pudding

Into the basin put the plums,
Stirabout, stirabout, stirabout!

Next the good white flour comes,
Stirabout, stirabout, stirabout!

Sugar and peel and eggs and spice.
Stirabout, stirabout, stirabout!

Mix them and fix them
and cook them twice.
Stirabout, stirabout, stirabout.

Unknown

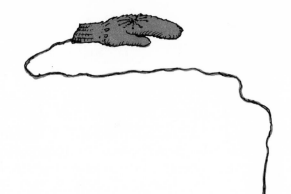

Presents

I wanted a rifle for Christmas,
   I wanted a bat and a ball,
I wanted some skates and a bicycle,
   But I didn't want mittens at all.

     I wanted a whistle
       And I wanted a kite.
     I wanted a pocketknife
       That shut up tight.
     I wanted some boots
       And I wanted a kit,
But I didn't want mittens one little bit.

I told them I didn't like mittens,
   I told them as plain as plain.
I told them I didn't WANT mittens,
   And they've given me mittens again!

Marchette Chute

Otto

It's Christmas Day. I did not get
The presents I had hoped for. Yet,
It is not nice to frown or fret.

To frown or fret would not be fair.
My Dad must never know I care.
It's hard enough for him to bear.

Gwendolyn Brooks

Christmas Tree

I'll find me a spruce
in the cold white wood
with wide green boughs
and a snowy hood.

I'll pin on a star
with five gold spurs
to mark my spruce
from the pines and firs.

I'll make me a score
of suet balls
to tie to my spruce
when the cold dusk falls.

And I'll hear next day
from the sheltering trees,
the Christmas carols
of the chickadees.

Aileen Fisher

Christmas Mouse

On the soft white snow
there's a thin white track
where a little mouse ran
but didn't come back . . .
for close to some rocks
where the tall weeds lean,
the little mouse changed
to a submarine!

At the foot of a fir
he ducked down under—
does he live in a house
down there, I wonder,
with a wreath on his door
for his friends to see,
and a sprig of spruce
for a Christmas tree?

Aileen Fisher

December Bird

If you were a bird . . .
and a Christmas tree
stood near the pane
for the world to see . . .
what would you think
when the wind was shrill,
and not even a crumb
on the window sill!

Aileen Fisher

The Twelve Days
of Christmas

On the first day of Christmas
My true love sent to me
A partridge in a pear tree.
—two turtle doves
—three French hens
—four calling birds
—five gold rings
—six geese a-laying
—seven swans a-swimming
—eight maids a-milking
—nine drummers drumming
—ten pipers piping
—eleven dancers dancing
—twelve lords a-leaping.

Unknown

Christmas Chant

Candle, candle,
  Burning bright
On our window
  Sill tonight,
Like the shining
  Christmas star
Guiding shepherds
  From afar,
Lead some weary
  Traveler here,
That he may share
  Our Christmas cheer.

Isabel Shaw

From

Christmas Bells

I heard the bells on Christmas Day
Their old, familiar carols play,
 And wild and sweet
 The words repeat
Of peace on earth, good-will to men!

    Henry Wadsworth Longfellow

New Year's Day

Last night, while we were fast asleep,
  The old year went away.
It can't come back again because
  A new one's come to stay.

Rachel Field

Ring Out, Wild Bells

Ring out, wild bells, to the wild sky,
    The flying cloud, the frosty light;
    The year is dying in the night;
Ring out, wild bells, let him die.

Ring out the old, ring in the new,
    Ring, happy bells, across the snow;
    The year is going, let him go;
Ring out the false, ring in the true.

Alfred Lord Tennyson

Valentine's Day

The aspens and the maples now
have lacy frost on every bough,

And through the woods the shadows go,
writing verses on the snow.

The tops of weeds are sealed up tight
in little envelopes of white,

And listen! in the frosty pines
snowbirds twitter Valentines.

Aileen Fisher

Valentine Greetings

Gold dust in the sky,
 Lacy clouds that dip about—
  Nature's valentine.

    Kathryn Sexton

To My Valentine

If apples were pears,
And peaches were plums,
And the rose had a different name;
If tigers were bears,
And fingers were thumbs,
I'd love you just the same!

    Unknown

Wearing of the Green

It ought to come in April,
or, better yet, in May
when everything is green as green—
I mean St. Patrick's Day.

With still a week of winter
this wearing of the green
seems rather out of season—
it's rushing things, I mean.

But maybe March *is* better
when all is done and said:
St. Patrick brings a promise,
a four-leaf-clover promise,
a green-all-over promise
of springtime just ahead!

Aileen Fisher

Irish

My father and mother were Irish,
And I am Irish, too;
I pipe you my bag of whistles,
And it is Irish, too.
I will sing with you in the morning,
And play with you at noon,
And dance with you in the evening
To a little Irish tune.
For my father and mother were Irish,
And I am Irish, too;
And here is my bag of whistles,
For it is Irish, too.

Edward J. O'Brien

Time for Rabbits

"Look!" says the catkin
in its gray hatkin.
"Look!" say the larks and the sparrows.
"The pasture is stirring,
the willows are purring,
and sunlight is shooting its arrows."

"Look!" wind is humming.
"Easter is coming.
Hear how the brooklet rushes.
It's time for the rabbits
with Easter-egg habits
to get out their paints and brushes."

Aileen Fisher

Easter

The air is like a butterfly
    With frail blue wings.
The happy earth looks at the sky
    And sings.

                    Joyce Kilmer

Easter Lily

If I gave you a flower
Lovely and chilly,
With petals of frost
And an ice-green well,
Would you know that I offered
An Easter lily
And begged you to drink
Its cool Easter smell?

                    Mary Britton Miller

Easter Morning

We went out on an Easter morning
Under the trees and the wide blue sky,
Up to the hill where the buds were
    swelling—
Mother, Father, and Puck and I.

And I had hopes that we'd see a rabbit,
A brown little one with a cotton tail,
So we looked in the woods and under the
    bushes,
And followed what seemed like a rabbit
    trail.

We peeked and poked. But there wasn't a
    rabbit
Wherever we'd look or wherever we'd go—
And then I remembered, and said,
    "NO WONDER,
Easter's their busiest day, you know!"

Aileen Fisher

Easter Parade

My button gloves are very white,
    My parasol is new,
My braids are braided nice and tight,
    And there are very few
Of all the people that I see
Who are as beautiful as me.

Marchette Chute

May Day

You heard the screen door open?
You heard the hinges squeak?
You heard the doorknob rattle—
before you got a peek?

You heard the porch boards creaking
beneath some hurrying feet?
You saw a little shadow
go flitting down the street?

And then you found a basket
with flowers inside, you say?
To think you had forgotten
it was the first of May!

Aileen Fisher

For a Dance

Round the Maypole dance about,
Dance your Ribbons in and out;
When they're plaited, then begin
To dance your Ribbons out and in.
Green and Yellow this way, that way Red and Blue,
Plait the Dance, unplait the Dance,
and plait the Dance anew!

Eleanor Farjeon

Fourth of July Night

Pin wheels whirling round
Spit sparks upon the ground,
And rockets shoot up high
And blossom in the sky—
Blue and yellow, green and red
Flowers falling on my head,
And I don't ever have to go
To bed, to bed, to bed!

Dorothy Aldis

Fireworks

They rise like sudden fiery flowers
That burst upon the night,
Then fall to earth in burning showers
Of crimson, blue, and white.

Like buds too wonderful to name,
Each miracle unfolds,
And catherine-wheels begin to flame
Like whirling marigolds.

Rockets and Roman candles make
An orchard of the sky,
Whence magic trees their petals shake
Upon each gazing eye.

James Reeves

The Wish

Each birthday wish
I've ever made
Really does come true,
Each year I wish
I'll grow some more
And every year
    I
       DO!

Ann Friday

The Birthday Child

Everything's been different
   All the day long,
Lovely things have happened,
   Nothing has gone wrong.

Nobody has scolded me,
   Everyone has smiled.
Isn't it delicious
   To be a birthday child?

Rose Fyleman

Growing Up

When I was seven
We went for a picnic
Up to a magic
Foresty place.
I knew there were tigers
Behind every boulder,
Though I didn't meet one
Face to face.

When I was older
We went for a picnic
Up to the very same
Place as before,
And all of the trees
And the rocks were so little
They couldn't hide tigers
Or *me* any more.

Harry Behn

Acknowledgments

Abelard-Schuman Ltd. for "Jack-o'-Lantern," "December Bird," and "Christmas Mouse" from *Runny Days, Sunny Days* by Aileen Fisher. Copyright © 1958 by Aileen Fisher.

Abingdon Press for "Halloween" from *I Rode the Black Horse Far Away* by Ivy O. Eastwick. Copyright © 1960 by Abingdon Press.

Dodd, Mead & Company for permission to reprint "The Birthday Child" from *Round the Mulberry Bush* by Rose Fyleman. Copyright 1928, 1955 by Rose Fyleman.

Doubleday & Company, Inc. for "New Year's Day" from *A Little Book of Days* by Rachel Field. Copyright 1927 by Doubleday & Company, Inc. Also for "Easter" by Joyce Kilmer, copyright 1914 by Harriet Monroe. From the book, *Trees and Other Poems* by Joyce Kilmer.

E. P. Dutton & Co., Inc. for "Easter Parade," "Presents," and "Hallowe'en" from *Around and About* by Marchette Chute. Published 1957 by E. P. Dutton & Co., Inc. Also for "Fireworks" from *The Blackbird in the Lilac* by James Reeves. Published by E. P. Dutton & Co., Inc.

Miss Aileen Fisher for her poems "I Like Fall," "December," "Christmas Tree," and "Easter Morning" from *That's Why,* published by Thomas Nelson & Sons, N.Y., 1946.

Harcourt, Brace & World, Inc. for "October Magic" from *Whispers and Other Poems* by Myra Cohn Livingston. Copyright © 1958, by Myra Cohn Livingston. Also for "Hallowe'en" and "Growing Up" from *The Little Hill* by Harry Behn. Copyright, 1949, by Harry Behn.

Harper & Row, Publishers, Inc. for "Otto" from *Bronzeville Boys and Girls* by Gwendolyn Brooks. Copyright © 1956 by Gwendolyn Brooks Blakely. And for "The Witches' Ride" from *The Rose on My Cake* by Karla Kuskin. Copyright © 1964 by Karla Kuskin.

Holt, Rinehart and Winston, Inc. for "Valentine Greetings" by Kathryn Sexton, from *Let Them Write Poetry,* by Nina Willis Walker, copyright © 1962 by Holt, Rinehart and Winston, Inc.

Mr. Langston Hughes for his poem "Carol of the Brown King," copyright 1958 by the Crisis Publishing Company, Inc., N.Y.

J. B. Lippincott Company for "In the Week When Christmas Comes" and "For a Dance" from *Poems for Children* by Eleanor Farjeon. Copyright © 1955 by Eleanor Farjeon. Published by J. B. Lippincott Company. "What Night Would It Be?" from *You Read to Me, I'll Read to You* by John Ciardi. Copyright © 1962 by John Ciardi. Published by J. B. Lippincott Company. "The Goblin" from *Picture Rhymes from Foreign Lands* by Rose Fyleman. Copyright 1935, 1963 by Rose Fyleman. Published by J. B. Lippincott Company.

Little, Brown and Company for "Was She a Witch?" from *Tirra Lirra* by Laura E. Richards. Copyright, 1932, by Laura E. Richards.

Harold Ober Associates for "Christmas Stocking" from *The Children's Bells* by Eleanor Farjeon. Copyright © 1960 by Eleanor Farjeon. Published by Henry Z. Walck, Inc. "For a Dance" and "In the Week When Christmas Comes" from *Poems for Children* by Eleanor Farjeon. Copyright 1951, 1955 by the author.

Oxford University Press for "Fireworks" from *The Blackbird in the Lilac* by James Reeves, published by Oxford University Press.

Plays, Inc., Publishers, for "Valentine's Day," "Wearing of the Green," and "May Day" from *Holiday Programs for Boys and Girls* by Aileen Fisher, copyright © 1953 by Aileen Fisher, Plays, Inc., Publishers, Boston, Mass.

G. P. Putnam's Sons for "Fourth of July Night" from *Hop, Skip, and Jump* by Dorothy Aldis. Copyright © 1934, 1961 by Dorothy Aldis. "What Am I?" from *Everything and Anything* by Dorothy Aldis. Copyright © 1925, 1926, 1927 by Dorothy Aldis.

Random House, Inc. for "Easter Lily," from *A Handful of Flowers,* by Mary Britton Miller. Copyright © 1959 by Pantheon Books, Inc., a Division of Random House, Inc.

Charles Scribner's Sons for "Christmas Eve" from *Open the Door* by Marion Edey. Copyright 1949 by Marion Edey. "Time for Rabbits" from *Cricket in a Thicket* by Aileen Fisher. Copyright © 1963 by Aileen Fisher.

Miss Isabel Shaw for her poem "Christmas Chant" which first appeared in *Jack and Jill* magazine. Copyright © 1949 by The Curtis Publishing Company.

The Society of Authors, in London, for "The Birthday Child" by Rose Fyleman.

The Viking Press, Inc. for "Words from an Old Spanish Carol" from *The Long Christmas* by Ruth Sawyer. Copyright 1941 by Ruth Sawyer.

Franklin Watts, Inc. for "To My Valentine," "Litany for Halloween," and "Beggars Rhyme" from *The First Book of Short Verse,* selected by Coralie Howard. Copyright © 1964 by Franklin Watts, Inc.

Index of Authors